HENRY WON

Written by Hazel Pacheco
Illustrated by Kim Sponaugle

Written by Hazel Pacheco
Illustrated by Kim Sponaugle

A STORY ABOUT JEALOUSY, SERENDIPITY, AND . . . FLAMENCO!

Henry and Friends Book 1

"Love is patient, love is kind. It does not envy, it does not boast, it is not proud." ~ 1 Corinthians 13:4

For my Aunt Thelma who gave me my first book, ignited my love of reading, and filled my world with wonder.
For Mireya, Mileva, Laura, and Moises who offered words of encouragement when I wondered.

Thank you to . . .
my family and friends for their constant loving support and for humoring my birdbrained ideas;
my Aunt Cecilia, who offered thoughtful suggestions;
my editor extraordinaire, Nevin Mays, who inspired me to write my best;
my cover designer and illustrator, Kim Sponaugle, who brought magic to my words; and,
my logo designer, Rosemarie Gillen, who added a dash class.

Other Books by Hazel Pacheco
That's How It Was: Operation Finders Keepers
Federico Exaggerated
Gloria Smiled (coming soon)
Ernesto Joked (coming soon)

Copyright

Pajarito Chronicles

Henry the quail
wondered about many
things. One morning, as he gazed at the surrounding trees and
brush known as the bosque (boss-kee), he wondered how
he might impress Gloria.

Henry's best pal, Ernesto, scurried over to Henry, thumped him on the back and, with a wink and a knowing look, kidded, "Hey Henry! Wondering why penguins always wear tuxedos?"

Henry scrunched his forehead.
"It's snow joke!" Ernesto belly laughed.
Before Henry could respond, a warning call sounded. "Kree kreee!"

A stranger strutted into the clearing.

He puffed out his chest, then rolling his r's he called, "I am *Fede-r-r-r-ri-co*. I was swept down a mighty river," he crowed, referring to the Rio Grande (ree-oh grahn-day). "I was captured and forced to live in a cage. Just this morning I pecked the lock and made my escape."

The entire covey was enchanted. They had never met such a brave, handsome roo who could peck a lock.

But Henry wondered.

Henry imagined Federico toppling over while trying to stand on one foot like a flamingo. Instead, Federico demonstrated his fancy foot stomping with a flourish of a raised wing and a shout of *"Olé!"* Henry was sure Federico had meant to say flamenco (fluh-men-ko), but his blunder went unnoticed by the rest of the covey.

After the applause, Federico smiled at Gloria . . . She smiled back.

Suddenly feeling invisible, Henry trudged to the old cottonwood tree and kicked up some leaves to unruffle his feathers and think.

Henry
wondered if he
might look more
exotic to
Gloria with a different crest.
Maybe a toupee like
the macaroni penguin . . .
a mohawk like the hoopoe . . .
a spikey crown like the
grey crowned crane . . . or
a ponytail like the Himalayan monal?
Hmm . . . a ponytail.
Henry wondered.

To imitate a ponytail, he tried leaning into the breeze to push
back his plume, but as soon as the breeze calmed,
his plume was back in his face.
Henry wondered.

He tried flying into the wind, but every time he landed, his plume fell forward.
Henry wondered.

He dipped his wing into a puddle and slicked back his plume. Ernesto happened by, did a double take and called, "Bad plume day?"

Henry's plume catapulted forward, then it bounced up and down.
Ernesto's body bounced up and down too—with laughter!—as he
scurried back to the covey.

Henry didn't have to wonder if trying to look sophisticated was a silly idea—it was!

Hmm . . . Henry was a good dancer. He wondered if Ernesto would teach him the blue-footed booby. Off to find Ernesto!

Lament

Author: Greg A. Vaughan and Alistair J. Rigg

Design, Illustration and Layout: Timothy Wickham, Richard Kunz, and Craig Williams

Cartography: Robert Lazzaretti

Chief Executive Officer: Jason Nelson

Chief Strategic Officer: Shirline Wilson

Chief Business Officer: Rachel Ventura

Special Thanks: Erik Mona, Lisa Stevens, James Jacobs and the Paizo staff and to Michael Kortes for his excellent ghost-story adventure, *The Haunting of Harrowstone*.

Legendary Games
524 SW 321st St.
Federal Way, WA 98023
makeyourgamelegendary.com

Welcome to Legendary Adventures

This product is a part of our line of support materials for extended Adventure Path-style campaign play for use with Paizo's Pathfinder Roleplaying Game. When you see the "Adventure Path Plug-In" logo at the top of a Legendary Games product, you can expect it is designed to fit directly with the themes of a particular Adventure Path campaign. The all-star team of designers here at Legendary Games is committed to bringing you—the busy GM or player—the absolute best third party support for your Pathfinder campaign. To deliver on that commit- ment, we've assembled the best of the best of current gaming authors, designers and layout experts so that you can feel comfortable that Legendary Games products will be the most creative, rules-legal and well-designed content you can find. Though Adventure Path Plug-Ins all share a theme with a specific Adventure Path campaign, they are designed to be easily incorporated into your home game regardless of what campaign you may be running.

Adventure Path campaigns contain amazing plots and stories written by the industry's best authors. But those adventures have space restrictions for print publication that often leave space either for alternatives for the busy GM or chances for the GM to personalize his or her game. The first installment of the current Adventure Path has just these issues—PCs need more small chances to earn experience and gain trust within the town. GMs need short adventures or locations that can be easily plugged in to the current adventure without disrupting its overall story. This adventure, The Fiddler's Lament, fills that need and more, providing the PCs with experience and the chance to gain Trust as well as the chance for the party to redeem a lost and tormented soul, bringing peace out of trag- edy for her and for the village as a whole. Their actions may lead the villagers themselves toward a path of deeper despair or transformative mercy, either way deepening their bond and investment with this place and its people.

Special Electronic Features

We've hyperlinked this product internally from the Table of Contents and externally with links to the official Pathfinder Reference Document as well as d2oPFSRD. If it is in the core rulebook, we generally didn't link to it unless the rule is an obscure one. The point is not to supersede the game books, but rather to help support you, the player, in accessing the rules, especially those from newer books or that you may not have memorized.

About Legendary Games

Legendary Games is an all-star team of authors and designers, founded by Clark Peterson of Necromancer Games, Inc. Legendary Games uses a cooperative, team-based approach to bring you, the Paizo fan, the best expansion material for your game. We are gamers and storytellers 1st, and we believe that passion shows in our products. So check us out, and Make Your Game Legendary!

Visit us on Facebook, follow us on Twitter, and check out our website at www.makeyourgamelegendary.com.

What You Will Find Inside
The Fiddler's Lament

Music hath charms to soothe the savage breast, it's true, but some music truly is the devil's music. An orphan raised by the traveling people, now full-grown but still lost and alone, must face once more the tragic curse that destroyed her past. Will her darkling music bring ruin to the village she now calls her home? Can the heroes earn the townsfolk's trust, or must innocence be sacrificed for the heroes to save town from the mysterious hauntings that plague a village huddled in the shadow of an accursed ruin?

This dark fantasy adventure is perfect for 1st-level characters using the 5th edition of the world's most famous role-playing game. The adventure can be played on its own or in combination with The Murmuring Fountain, or as part of the beginning of a horror-themed Adventure Path campaign.

TABLE OF CONTENTS

not provide enough experience in and of itself for the PCs to increase in level substantially, but it provides several challenges and rewards, including gaining Trust within the town.

ADVENTURE BACKGROUND

Alhindriosa had a fey spirit for even the folk of the Elven Kingdom. Her parents said she had her head more in other worlds than in this one as she sang and danced her way through life, sprightly even for an elf. When her parents died in a tragic boating accident, she was subdued for their funeral, but even that fugue was short-lived as she soon went back to her ways of prancing across meadows to stir the butterflies and singing nonsensical songs to the birds. Many of the elves thought her stricken or possessed, and ultimately none were anything but secretly relieved when upon reaching the beginnings of adulthood she up and left the elves to explore the greater world outside their hedged realm.

Alhindriosa wandered for weeks, gradually making her way around the great inner sea before finally falling in with a band of traveling folk headed north. In this people of dusken skin and dervish dances, Alhindriosa had finally found a kindred spirit. They knew the ways of the night song and the dance of the moonlight upon the water; they too could hear the music in the crackle of the campfire and freedom of Nature as it flowed through their veins in an expression of purest joy, devoid of thought or artifice. In turn, the Wanderers accepted her as one of their own and allowed her to dance to the sound of their fiddle and tambourine as they traveled the rugged countryside of the North.

For more than a decade Alhindri, as she became known, danced among the Wanderers, and even they had to recognize something different about her— something special that transcended the mundane and touched on

offered to take her in marriage and make her a respected matron of their tribe, but she gently rebuffed them all content in their company alone, seeking

neither companionship nor station—known to all the towns they visited as the dancing elf maid of the Wandering Folk.

Unfortunately though the years of an elf are long, her state of bliss came to an end all too soon. One evening as their caravan camped in the wilderness, a dark stranger came into their midst. Swathed all in cloak, scarf, and a wide-brimmed hat, though it was a warm spring night, he requested the hospitality of their fire. This was begrudgingly given but the elder matron of the tribe immediately made the ward against the Evil Eye at the stranger, and all fell silent in his presence. Perturbed at the end of the festivities the stranger demanded that the fiddler strike up a tune and that the elf maid dance for him. Alhindri thought that he seemed handsome enough from what she could see, but before she could acquiesce to his request—nay demand—the strangest thing happened. Lothiaro, the head of the caravan, took his fiddle and smashed it upon a rock claiming that none of the Wandering Folk would play for the Dark Stranger and that none under his protection would dance before him—as it has always been among the Wandering Folk, and as it would always be.

Alhindri did not quite understand what was going on and watched in a strangely calm daze as the Dark Stranger proclaimed, "So be it," and proceeded to gruesomely slaughter the Wanderers—her kin of the last several years— with his bare hands before her very eyes. Some of them sought to fight; others tried to flee. It mattered not, for the stranger moved with a speed and savagery unmatched by mortal limbs. In moments, the gory massacre was done, and the blood-slicked stranger stood before Alhindri. She found that she could not look up into his mesmerizing eyes and only stared dumbly at the ground where she noticed the curious detail that he had cloven hooves instead of feet.

will meet again, you and I.

Then he was gone in the darkness, and Alhindri found that she couldn't bring herself to move for some time but simply sat and stared at the dew-stained grass where he had stood and the imprint of two cloven hooves that remained faintly visible.

When villagers from the nearby town of Raven came upon the scene of the massacre three days later, Alhindri still sat as she had, staring at the ground, silent and unresponsive, her cheeks hollow from hunger and thirst and her brow burned from days in the unrelenting sun. The villagers buried the traveling people in the consecrated ground of their town cemetery to prevent them from arising again to trouble the living and took the elven waif in out of the kindness of their hearts, thinking her one of the forlorn members of her race presumably in shock over what she must have witnessed. They nursed Alhindri back to health but soon learned that her injuries were more of her spirit than to her body. She never spoke nor emerged from her silent stupor. Finally, realizing that they could do no more for the young elf, one of the local councilmen paid out of his generosity to have her transported to a hospital in a distant city where she could be cared for in hopes that she would eventually emerge from her fugue and be able to tell what had occurred to the Wanderers she had been with.

There Alhindri waited, known only as the Raven Patient, passed from hospital to prison to asylum, silent and alone for 85 years...until today. In the darkest hour of the early morning, Alhindri opened her eyes to discover a dark-cloaked figure standing in her cell with her. He called her by name and told her it was time for her to return to her lost kin and dance for them once more. She was fascinated, as he spoke, by the pair of cloven hooves that peeked out from beneath his cloak but became even more astonished when he handed her a meticulously cared for violin that in her mind's eye she recognized at

The Fiddler's Lament takes place in the town of Raven near a haunted prison. The enigmatic Dark Stranger, for reasons of his own, has brought Alhindri back to the region where he slaughtered her adopted kin and has provided her not with the beloved fiddle of her former protector but an infernal instrument called the Rebec Malevolenti, crafted in the pits of Hell with the sole purpose to bring ruin upon mortals. With this instrument, Alhindri heedlessly summons forth the dead from their rest and causes them to descend like a plague upon the unsuspecting town of Raven nearby. Only with the destruction of the fiddle can the plague of zombies and worse be stopped.

The adventure begins as the PCs, who have already come to the town of Raven for their own reasons, make their way to the general store to gather supplies.

once as being that which had belonged to Lothiaro, made whole once more.

Immediately the color returned to Alhindri's face and her life as she took the beloved instrument in her hands. She didn't even notice when the Dark Stranger wrapped his cowl around her and she found herself no longer in her lonely cell but standing upon a hill covered in tombs, surrounded by ancient unmarked graves. In the pre-light of dawn she gave no more thought to her surroundings than to a gnat as she touched bow to fiddle and began to play. The fiddle had never been her instrument, but she had been around it enough to pick up a bit, and as she played upon Lothiaro's beloved violin she found that it practically played itself. She soon lost herself to the music and began to dance as of old...and she did not dance alone as her long-lost traveling folk kin rose from the ground to join her.

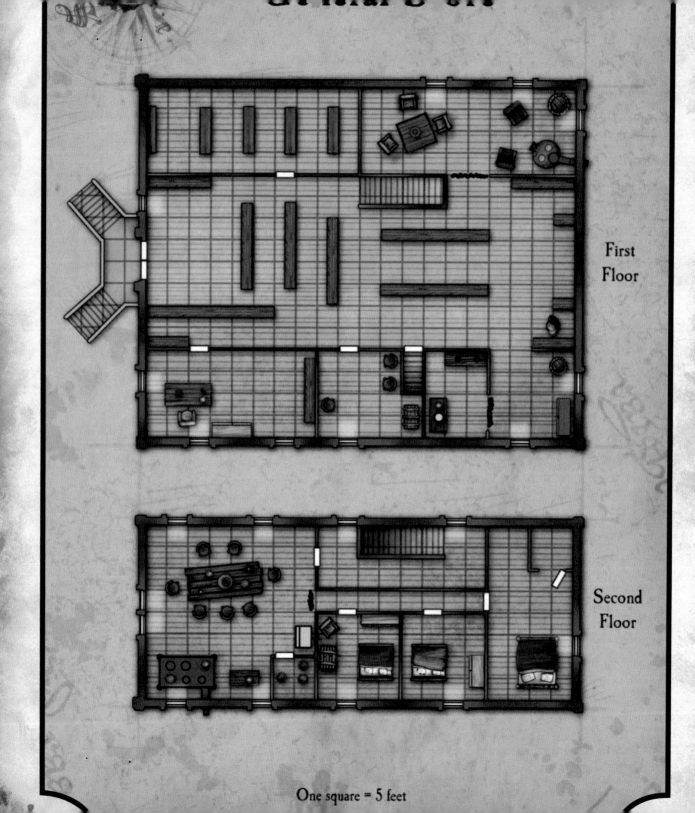

First
Floor

Second
Floor

One square = 5 feet

The Fiddler's Lament takes place in the town of Raven near the haunted prison described in the Adventure Path. The enigmatic Dark Stranger, for reasons of his own, has brought Alhindri back to the region where he slaughtered her adopted kin and has provided her not with the beloved fiddle of her former protector but an infernal instrument called the Rebec Malevolenti, crafted in the pits of Hell with the sole purpose to bring ruin upon mortals. With this instrument Alhindri heedlessly summons forth the dead from their rest and causes them to descend like a plague upon the unsuspecting town of Raven nearby. Only with the destruction of the fiddle can the plague of zombies and worse be stopped.

The adventure begins as the PCs, who have already come to the town of Raven for their own reasons, make their way to the general store to gather supplies for their ongoing investigation. It can begin at any time during the Adventure Path module but should probably occur early in their stay in Raven before they've had a chance to do much poking around in the nearby haunted prison. This can give them some much needed experience as well as some foreshadowing of things soon to come.

eastern horizon as you make your way through long shadows across the town square. The village itself is coming awake as goodwives push their sleepy-eyed children out the door to begin the day's chores. The usual sounds of cock's crow and the occasional dog bark are joined this morning by something unexpected. Floating lightly upon the morning breeze is the sound of a hauntingly beautiful melody as if the world's saddest fiddler were out this morning plying his bow to catgut in a dirge for the day to come. Who the mysterious player might be is unguessed but the music, though mournful, is not unpleasant.

Though it is morning, the PCs are assumed to be wearing their normal gear and equipment as befits an adventuring party. Their reasons for visiting the general store are important but should just be to pick up some mundane supplies or equipment. Unfortunately, while there they learn that there is more to the fiddler's music than they know and that its effects have come to visit upon the town.

VISIT FROM GRAMMY (CR 1)

The storekeep and a local gaffer chat idly near the front counter talking about the strange music, which has apparently been heard across parts of town since before dawn, speculating as to who could be the source. The storekeep's wife stocks shelves while their young girls run around playing chase. You once again eye the suit of fine plate armor that stands near the back of the store, wondering what kind of coin it would take to get the storekeep to part with it—you've heard him mention that it belonged to his wife's long-deceased grandfather from back when he fought for the Crown.

As one of the young girls opens the cellar door to fetch a bag of herbs for her mother, you hear her small child's voice suddenly exclaim with delight, "Grammy?!" to which the storekeep's wife patiently explains, "No, dear. You know Grammy and Grampy passed on from the fever last winter. She's not waiting in the cellar for you."

forward, but you are diverted from further investigation by the sound of the heavy, slow tread of bare feet climbing the cellar stair and the look of delight still on the young girl's face as she shouts, "It is Grammy!" at something behind the cellar door that you can't see yet. As the suit of armor clatters to the floor at your feet and you see standing in the alcove behind it the worm-eaten corpse of what was once a gray-bearded old man, you can only think to yourself, "And this must be Grampy."

Then the screaming begins.

The map shows the floor plan of the general store, which is location "F" on the Adventure Path's town map. The shelves hold only mundane equipment and supplies, though the waist-high shelves and front counter do provide cover to anyone behind them and require a DC 6 Acrobatics check to leap over them headfirst (DC 12 without at least a 10-foot running start), or a DC 12 (DC 24 with no run) to leap atop them. They can be easily climbed over with a move action, but it provokes attacks of opportunity.

Creatures: The first of the undead brought forth by Alhindri's bone fiddle that the PCs encounter are indeed the zombies of Grammy and Grampy come back to visit their young folk. They crept into the store before light while the owners were busy elsewhere and instinctively took up hiding places as they had once done to play with their grandchildren. The sound of the young girls playing has brought them out of their hiding places but has also triggered their instinct to destroy all living creatures, so playtime is over. They lurch to attack whoever is closest. Hopefully this will be the PCs as the storekeep's wife grabs the young child and bolts for the stairs to the upper floor while the storekeep gathers up his other four older girls and hustles them that way as well. The gaffer likewise scoots out the front door leaving the PCS to deal with the zombie menace. They attack and pursue until destroyed.

"Zombie")

Development: When the PCs have finished with the zombies, they can hear the sound of screams from out in the town square with a successful DC 10 Perception check. However, immediately after they hear the shrill screams of the storekeep's wife and their five little girls coming from upstairs. Encourage the PCs to stick together unless they have more than four PCs as they decide if they will go outside to see what is going on or if they wish to head upstairs to face the more immediate threat.

Lingering Shadows (CR 1/2)

If the PCs head upstairs in the general store, they find it still dark and shuttered from the previous night's repose. The sound of whimpering cries and shrill little screams come from the master bedroom. A single candle lights the room and just a hint of dawn light leaks through the heavily curtained window. Across the room, behind the bed, huddle the storekeep and his entire family.

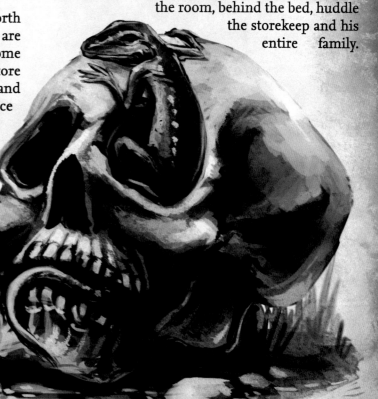

Creature: Another dire visitor from the town cemetery has made its way into here. It is a lesser shadow, much like its normal brethren but weaker and more stunted in its power. It lurches forth to attack as soon as the PCs enter, trying to get at the helpless family but willing to take on adventurers if they interfere. As long as the room remains in dim light, the lesser shadow has concealment against the PCs. If anyone thinks to open the curtain (the storekeep can do so if they PCs think to tell him), the bright dawn light floods into the room and removes this concealment for the creature. In addition, it must make a DC 10 Will check each round to stay and fight or flee back into the closet and out through the walls of the house to find some shadowy corner of the town in which to hide. If it flees, it is not encountered again in this adventure.

LESSER SHADOW	CR 1/2

XP 200
The Tome of Horrors Complete 541 CE Medium undead (incorporeal)
Init +2; **Senses** darkvision 60 ft.; Perception +8

DEFENSE

AC 14, touch 14, flat-footed 11 (+1 deflection, +1 dodge, +2 Dex)
hp 6 (1d8+2)
Fort +2, **Ref** +2, **Will** +2
Defensive Abilities channel resistance +1, incorporeal, shadow blend; **Immune** undead traits

OFFENSE

Speed fly 40 ft. (good)
Melee incorporeal touch +2 (1 Strength damage)

STATISTICS

Str —, **Dex** 15, **Con** —, **Int** 5, **Wis** 10, **Cha** 14
Base Atk +0; **CMB** +2; **CMD** 15
Feats Dodge
Skills Fly +6, Perception +8, Stealth +6
SQ phantom noises

living foe. A creature drained to Strength 0 by a lesser shadow dies. This is a negative energy effect.

Shadow Blend (Ex) In any light condition less than bright light, the lesser shadow's form blends into the surrounding shadows, granting it concealment.

Development: If the PCs rescue the storekeep and his family, they receive an additional 10% discount off of any other discounts or markups they may receive when they shop in the general store.

FIGHT OF THE OLD DOG (CR 3)

When the PCs emerge from the general store, whether they have defeated the zombies and lesser shadow within or not, they witness the following scene.

The mysterious fiddle plays on, barely audible above the ruckus that has arisen in the town square. Townsfolk flee everywhere with lurching undead horrors shambling along after them. Most people seem to be managing to lock themselves within their homes and businesses causing the walking dead to wander elsewhere in search of prey, but in the center of the square, where stands the old gazebo, a different scene unfolds. A number of disembodied, clawlike hands clamber across the ground towards the structure and up its rails. Within stands the town's mangy stray dog that has been adopted by the children. As the crawling hands approach menacingly the dog stands its ground growling at them and blocking the way towards a small group of children behind who it who at the same time appear to be trying to get past the dog with their sticks and play swords in order to bravely defend it from the approaching horrors. None of the townsfolk seem to have noticed this yet, and it is only a matter of time before the dog and children find themselves in trouble.

dog is doing well to hold the children back and ward off the undead creatures, one group or the other will soon manage to get past its defenses and result in a tragedy for the town. If the PCs hurry, though, they will be able to intervene in time to save them. The crawling hands will turn on the newcomers while the dog will bolt causing the children to squeal and chase after it, leading them to safety. If the PCs find themselves in over their heads, the dog can return to fight alongside them (treat as a riding dog)

CRAWLING HANDS (4)   CR 1/2

XP 200

hp 9 (*Pathfinder Roleplaying Game Bestiary* "Crawling Hand")

Development: Once the crawling hands have been dealt with, the PCs can take stock of the situation around town. A few zombies wander hither and yon but without any apparent real motivation, and with most of the villagers safely locked up in their homes they are out of immediate danger. Checking with the sheriff reveals that he is away at one of the outlying farms this morning and most of his deputies are currently off duty tending to their own farming chores. There doesn't seem to be anyone around in any better position to defend the town than the PCs themselves. All of the walking dead are recognizable to various townspeople as their departed family and friends who are supposed to be safely interred in the town cemetery to the north. No one knows why they would be up and about like this.

To the south of the square, the moneylenders have stationed their troop of bodyguards outside the door to their establishment, and this group of eight veteran warriors (human warrior 4) has dispatched a half dozen of the walking dead themselves. They put the finishing touches on a seventh as the PCs watch. One of the moneylenders leans out the second-floor window of his shop and shouts to the PCs that he will pay them 50 gp each if they will stay and defend his shop alongside his guards. At the same time, the haunting music continues to drift from the north and the sounds of additional shouts and screams can be heard from that direction.

If the PCs choose to take up post alongside the moneylenders' mercenaries, they receive a chorus of boos from any of the villagers watching from their windows. Every 10 minutes another 1d4+1 zombies will wander through the town square and attack while the sounds of battle elsewhere in town will eventually die down to an ominous silence with only the fiddle music as accompaniment. This can go on for days with the sheriff and all his deputies eventually arriving and falling to the endless waves of zombies. At some point the PCs will need to either give the town up for dead or head north to try and stop the fiddling that seems to be somehow connected to the zombie plague.

If the PCs head north proceed with "Extra! Extra! Read All About It!" If they head south to reach the temple or some other area of town, see "A Slimy Skeleton in the Closet" for details of what is going on elsewhere.

This event occurs at the posting pole (the location marked as "B" on the Adventure Path's town map) at the east end of the covered bridge.

The posting pole lies just ahead, a thick tree trunk, stripped of branches, sawed off at head height on a tall man, and set upright in the ground at the end of the covered bridge so that notices and broadsheets can be tacked to it for all to see. The young lad that you recognize as being responsible for hanging the notices crouches at the top of the pole trying to stay out of reach of two clay-encrusted skeletons that swipe at him with jagged claws. His stack of posting notices lies scattered on the ground. Sitting astride a skeletal horse nearby is another skeleton, this one armored in a rusted breastplate. A frayed noose dangles from its broken neck, and a cracked leather eye patch covers one eye. The other two skeletons likewise have the remains of nooses hanging from them.

Creatures: The town's posting boy has run afoul of a group of malevolent dead raised by the music of the Rebec Malevolenti. The bandit Kurchega was caught and hanged at the covered bridge by the townsfolk of Raven 40 years ago after plaguing the area with his bloody raids for an entire year. Two of his accomplices were hanged with him, and before he died he watched the townsfolk slaughter his prized mare. All were buried in the river embankment near the bridge in unmarked graves so that their memory would be forgotten by all. With the coming of the supernatural music, they have dug forth from their clay resting places. They came upon the posting boy unawares and have been making sport of him at Kurchega's orders until he grows bored and orders the kill. When they see the party they turn to attack. If the PCs have been having an easy go of things so far, include the skeletal mount as a combatant. Otherwise it serves Kurchega as a mount but does not enter the fray as a combatant itself and likewise crumbles to dust when the bandit chief if destroyed.

Champion")

SKELETONS (2)   CR 1/2

XP 135

hp 4 (*Pathfinder Roleplaying Game Bestiary* "Skeleton")

SKELETAL MOUNT   CR 1

XP 400

Advanced heavy horse skeleton[AP44]

NE Large undead

Init +9; **Senses** darkvision 60 ft.; Perception +0

DEFENSE

AC 17, touch 13, flat-footed 13 (+2 armor, +4 Dex, +2 natural, −1 size)

hp 9 (2d8)

Fort +0, **Ref** +5, **Will** +3

DR 5/bludgeoning; **Immune** cold, undead traits

OFFENSE

Speed 50 ft.

Melee bite +5 (1d4+5), 2 hooves +0 (1d6+2)

Space 10 ft.; **Reach** 5 ft.

STATISTICS

Str 20, **Dex** 20, **Con** —, **Int** —, **Wis** 10, **Cha** 10

Base Atk +1; **CMB** +7; **CMD** 22 (26 vs. trip)

Feats Improved Initiative[B]

Gear broken chain shirt barding

Development: If the posting boy is rescued, he immediately runs to his father's restaurant at the river's edge and tells him everything that transpires. The heroism of the PCS will then appear in tracts on the posting poles over the next several days.

west of the covered bridge just north of location M4 on Adventure Path's town map. Here the PCs run into Rufio, one of the acolytes (see "Raven's Rest" for stats) from the temple of the goddess of fate and prophecy, the deity venerated by the locals. He has a small cut across his forehead and is much disheveled but otherwise seems none the worse for wear. He is running north towards the cemetery, but sags to his haunches out of breath in relief when he sees the PCs.

In between gasps for breath, he explains that Father Grimble and most of the acolytes went to the cemetery early this morning before the ghostly music started in order to prepare for a funeral. They have not returned. Just a short while ago a group of walking dead overran the temple and killed the other acolyte there while he fled out the back. He says he has got to get to the cemetery to alert Father Grimble and bring him back. He says that on his way here he passed Councilor Murik's home and saw that they were having some sort of trouble. He kept going but promised he would send help as soon as he found Father Grimble. He now begs the PCs to head to Murik's house and help him while he goes to fetch the good father. He will not force the PCs to go that way but will give them the pouch of seven scrolls of cure light wounds (CL 1st) that he snatched before fleeing the temple if they agree to do so. He will also expend the last of his own cure spells and channel energies to heal the PCs (assume he has enough to bring them all to maximum hit points). If the PCs refuse to go help Councilor Murik, he will not force them to but does not give them the scrolls. He will still heal them, though.

If the PCs agree to head south, Rufio tells them to not bother going to the temple as it is overrun. As soon as they help out the councilor, he asks them to join him up at the cemetery so that Father Grimble and the other acolytes can link up with them to sweep the undead from the town.

If the PCs head south to Councilor Murik's house, proceed with the following. If they instead follow the acolyte to the cemetery skip to "Raven's Rest".

the sound of shattering glass and breaking furniture. Soon the aged councilor himself hobbles out onto the front porch, slams the door behind him, and huddles behind a large flower urn to hide. Following him a slimy apparition that appears to be wearing the finery of a wealthy man, a wealthy man with a striking resemblance to the councilor himself, steps through the door as if it wasn't there and leaves a spot of viscous ooze upon the hardwood. As the dripping creature lurches towards the cowering councilor, you see that the ghostly image of a hatchet protrudes from the back of the apparition's head. When the councilor catches sight of you he shouts in a raspy, fear-choked voice, "Help me! I didn't do it! He thinks I'm my father!"

Creature: Councilor Murik is currently being menaced by the ectoplasmic remains of one of his own ancestors, Pecrit Murik, foully murdered many years ago and now come back to visit revenge upon the wrong descendant. The ectoplasmic creature attempts to slay Councilor Murik unless the PCs interpose themselves between it and the feeble old councilor. If the PCs do not do so, assume that the creature manages to finish the old man off in 3 rounds before wandering off to vent its rage elsewhere. If the PCs manage to damage the creature, it turns its attention towards them. The councilor's serving staff remains hidden in the house and does not emerge to assist until the battle is over.

PECRIT MURIK   CR 1/2

XP 200
Male ectoplasmic[AP43] human
CE Medium undead
Init +0; **Senses** darkvision 60 ft.; Perception –1

DEFENSE

AC 12, touch 10, flat-footed 12 (+2 natural)
hp 8 (1d8+4)
Fort +0, **Ref** +0, **Will** +2
DR 5/slashing; **Immune** undead traits

OFFENSE

Speed 30 ft.
Melee slam +3 (1d4+3 plus horrifying ooze)

Str 16, **Dex** 11, **Con** —, **Int** —, **Wis** 10, **Cha** 12
Base Atk +0; **CMB** +3; **CMD** 13
Feats Toughness[B]
SQ phase lurch

SPECIAL ABILITIES

Horrifying Ooze (Su) Any creature that is struck by the ectoplasmic crea ture's slam attack must make a DC 11 Will save or become shaken for 1d4 rounds. The save DC is Charisma-based.

Phase Lurch (Su) An ectoplasmic creature has the ability to pass through walls or material obstacles. In order to use this ability, the ectoplasmic creature must begin and end its turn outside of whatever wall or obstacle it is moving through. An ectoplasmic creature cannot move through corporeal creatures with this ability, and its movement speed is halved while moving through a wall or obstacle. Slimy mucus that lingers for 1 minute marks the spot on a wall where an ectoplasmic creature entered and exited it.

Development: If the ectoplasmic creature is defeated and Councilor Murik survives, the old politician emerges form hiding and thanks the PCs profusely for their aid. He sheepishly admits that the creature was undoubtedly his grandfather, Pecrit Murik, a vile and abusive drunk. According to family lore, the councilor's own father Alberit waylaid his grandfather in the woods with a hatchet when he was drunk and buried him in a hidden grave somewhere on the property. The councilor never knew where the grave was or even if the legend was true, and Alberit has been dead for over 40 years, however, based on the apparition that appeared seeking vengeance it would seem that the old tale was true. Here the councilor clears his throat awkwardly and states that it would be quite an embarrassment to his family and the town if it was revealed that one of their councilors was the son of a murderer. He assures the PCs that he will do all he can to make their stay in Raven as welcoming as possible if they would, how shall we say, use the utmost discretion in any matters pertaining to what they have learned here. Regardless of their

RAVEN'S REST (CR 2)

The cemetery lies a short distance north of the town and is not shown on the town map, though the Adventure Path does provide a map of the cemetery itself. When the PCs arrive, they approach from the southwest gate. If they choose to enter by a different gate, use the same encounter but relocate it to there. If the PCs accompanied the acolyte, then omit the portion in parentheses from the following description.

The source of the day's trouble lies ahead, the Raven's Rest Cemetery. It rises from the moor like a well-tended garden of stone, rising beyond its gates past row upon row of headstones to a low hill crowned by a circle of ancient tomb vaults. The fiddling floats over the cemetery much louder than elsewhere in town and achieves an almost manic quality. Everywhere across the cemetery tombstones tumble over and the earth churns where things that ought lie still struggle to emerge from the cold ground. Yet atop the hill a single figure can be seen racing around, jumping to and fro in time to the music. There lies your quarry, and a road runs straight to the top if only you can win past the emerging hordes of the unquiet dead. From the brush beside the gate steps a foul creature, obviously once a wolf, its skin hangs in ragged strips from it moldering hide with ribs showing through the gaps in its bloated, putrid flesh. (There is fresh blood on its jaws, and the torn robes of a temple acolyte beside the road hide the remains of the wolf's recent handiwork.)

If Rufio preceded the PCs here, then he was paralyzed by the ghoul wolf when he attempted to enter the cemetery. If the party instead accompanied him here, then his stats are included under "Development" below. He does not know exactly where Father Grimble and the other acolytes were making their funeral preparations but assumes the high ground at the boneyard's center is as good a place to start looking as any. He will assist in any combats unless you feel the PCs are having too easy a time of it, in which case he hangs back and stays out of any fights.

summons of the *Rebel Malevolent*, it has arisen as a ghoul wolf and attacks anyone it meets, fighting until destroyed.

GHOST WOLF · CR 2

XP 600
The Tome of Horrors Complete 649
CE Medium undead
Init +2; **Senses** darkvision 60 ft., scent; Perception +9

DEFENSE

AC 14, touch 12, flat-footed 12 (+2 Dex, +2 natural)
hp 18 (4d8)
Fort +1, **Ref** +3, **Will** +6
DR channel resistance +2; **Immune** undead traits

OFFENSE

Speed 50 ft.
Melee bite +7 (1d6+4 plus paralysis plus trip)
Special Attacks paralysis (1d4+2 rounds, DC 12, elves are immune to this effect)

STATISTICS

Str 17, **Dex** 15, **Con** —, **Int** 6, **Wis** 14, **Cha** 10
Base Atk +3; **CMB** +6; **CMD** 18 (22 vs. trip)
Feats Skill Focus (Perception), Weapon Focus (bite)
Skills Perception +9, Stealth +6, Survival +2 (+6 tracking by scent)

Development: If the PCS did not accompany Rufio the acolyte here, then he is lying wounded by the edge of the road where he fell after being attacked by the ghoul wolf. He is currently paralyzed, but the effect will wear off in 2 more rounds. He has a single potion of cure light wounds on him (which the PCs could use to cure his wounds if they chose) plus the pouch of scrolls if he did not already give it to them. If he was with the PCs all along, then he is not wounded.

LN Medium humanoid (human)
Init +1; **Senses** Perception +6

DEFENSE

AC 13, touch 11, flat-footed 12 (+1 armor, +1 Dex, +1 shield)
hp 13, currently 7 (2d8+1)
Fort +3, **Ref** +1, **Will** +5

OFFENSE

Speed 30 ft.
Melee light mace +0 (1d6–1)
Special Attacks channel positive energy (all used for the day), spontaneous casting (cure spells)
Domain Spell-Like Abilities (CL 2nd) At will—lore keeper (melee touch +0) 5/day—*rebuke death*
Spells Prepared (CL 2nd) None currently
D domain spell; Domains Healing, Knowledge

STATISTICS

Str 9, **Dex** 12, **Con** 10, **Int** 11, **Wis** 14, **Cha** 12
Base Atk +1; **CMB** +0; **CMD** 11
Feats Alertness[B], Self-Sufficient
Skills Heal +9, Knowledge (religion) +5, Perception +6, Sense Motive +4, Survival +4
Languages Common
Combat Gear *potion of cure light wounds*; **Other Gear** padded armor, light wooden shield, light mace, silver holy symbol

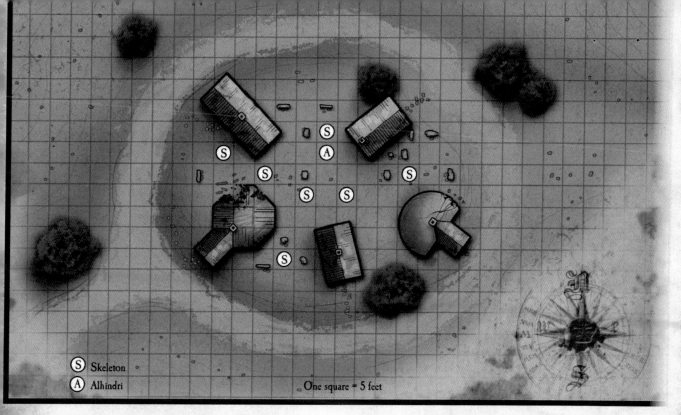

S Skeleton
A Alhindri

One square = 5 feet

CEMETERY HILL (CR VARIES)

The Raven's Rest cemetery is large and sprawling with multiple pathways leading through ranks of headstones, but one path in particular leads directly to the crown of the hill at its center. Everywhere the PCs look they see grave's churning as their occupants slowly unearth themselves or open graves where the occupants have already departed. Straying from the path or exploring the cemetery has a 50% chance of an encounter with an undead creature each round (see table in the "Rebec Malevolenti" sidebar to determine what kind). Searching for Father Grimble and the missing acolytes will likewise cause these random encounters.

When the PCs climb the hill read the following.

A cluster of aged stone vaults stand atop the hill overgrown with creepers and high wild grass. It seems this portion of the cemetery is older and gets less tending than other areas. Barely visible in the tall grass are a number of headstones, cracked and crumbling with age and canted at wild angles from their long years exposed to the elements. Dancing among them like a vision out of a fever dream is an elven maid. She is barefoot with long, lithe limbs and wears a tattered and stained hospital shift and the ragged remains of a straight jacket that no longer restrains her. In her arms she holds a narrow-bodied traveling folk fiddle which she plays energetically as she dances about. Her face is the very picture of transported bliss as her eyes dance with gaiety and unbidden laughs actually burst forth from her mouth from time to time.

Though the elf may be the image of grace and joy, the effects of her playing cannot be denied, as rotten and skeletal arms continue to rise from the ground around her, clawing their way to the surface as they sway in perfect time with the frenetic music.

Unknown Wanderer. Foully murdered. A DC 10 Knowledge (local) identifies Wanderer as the name for the enigmatic traveling folk bands that wander the North. A DC 20 Knowledge (local or history) recalls tales of Alhindri's band massacred near Raven and of the lone elf maid survivor who never spoke a word and was eventually locked up and forgotten. The headstones do not impede movement but do provide cover to Small creatures.

Creatures: Here at the summit of the hill the PCs have found Alhindri, totally enthralled in joy as she plays the fiddle provided for her by the Dark Stranger. She is blissfully unaware of the effects it is having on the surrounding graveyard and cannot be interrupted in her playing. And since the fiddle provides her with

herself are pointless as it is the *Rebec Malevolent* that must be destroyed to end the zombie plague. In the meantime, concealed among the tall grass at the points marked on the map are the skeletal remains of her former traveling folk companions. They still wear the tattered remains of their distinctive Wanderer garb and rise up to defend Alhindri from anyone that attempts to interfere with her playing. She uses one move action each round to dance about atop the hill and another to play her fiddle. These do not provoke attacks of opportunity unless she moves through a threatened square, which she will attempt to avoid doing if possible. She does not otherwise react to the PCs' presence. There are a total of seven skeletons guarding Alhindri. Every 2 rounds, another traveling folk skeleton emerges from the

attacks of opportunity in the round that it emerges, though it has concealment in the tall grass. Choose the spot of its emergence at random. When the Rebec Malevolenti is destroyed, all remaining undead in the cemetery and nearby town fall dead once again and no more emerge.

SKELETONS (7 OR MORE)   CR 1/3

XP 135
hp 4 (*Pathfinder Roleplaying Game Bestiary* "Skeleton")

ALHINDRI

XP 400
Female elf commoner 3
N Medium humanoid (elf)
Init +2; **Senses** low-light vision; Perception +0

DEFENSE

AC 16, touch 13, flat-footed 13 (+2 Dex, +1 dodge, +3 natural)
hp 7 (3d6–3)
Fort +0, **Ref** +3, **Will** –1; +2 vs. enchantment
Defensive Abilities false life, freedom of movement; **DR** 5/magic; **Immune** sleep, undead traits

OFFENSE

Speed 30 ft.
Melee unarmed strike –1 (1d3–2/nonlethal)

STATISTICS

Str 7, **Dex** 14, **Con** 10, **Int** 9, **Wis** 6, **Cha** 16
Base Atk +1; **CMB** –1; **CMD** 12 (16 vs. sunder)
Feats Dodge, Skill Focus (Perform [dance])
Skills Linguistics +0, Perception +0, Perform (dance) +9, Perform (string instruments) +4
Languages Common, Elven, Wanderer
Gear *Rebec Malevolenti*

---

of opportunities for the PCs to accrue Trust Points and even a few for them to lose them. These are outlined below. These points are added or subtracted for the entire party even if only one or two PCs were involved in the specific action—the party gains and loses the Trust Points together.

TABLE 1—1: TRUST POINTS

Trust Points	PC Actions
+1	Choosing to assist the storekeep's family before going outside to investigate
+1	Saving the children in the town square from the crawling hands
+1	Saving the town's pet dog from the crawling hand
–2	Staying to help the moneylenders rather than immediately moving on to assist others in the town
+2	Saving the post boy
+1	Choosing to help Councilor Murik
+3	Keeping Councilor Murik's secret confidential
+4	Ending the undead menace caused by the fiddler
–1	Convincing the townsfolk to spare Alhindri's life

Aura strong necromancy [evil]; **CL** 12th

Slot —; **Price** —; **Weight** 3 lbs.

DESCRIPTION

This is a three-stringed fiddle made with a narrowboat-shaped body and a horsehair bow. Its finish has the cracked polish of old bone, and when stared at intently tiny glowing red lettering can be seen to swirl about just beneath its varnish, never staying still long enough to read the infernal writing. When played by someone with at least 1 rank in Perform (stringed instruments), the rebec grants the following powers to the fiddler for as long as she plays:

- The player is provided with a +3 bonus to natural armor and DR 5/magic The player receives the immunities associated with undead traits, though she does not actually become undead or become otherwise susceptible to posi-tive energy attacks.

- The player becomes engrossed in the playing and suffers a –4 penalty to Perception while doing so.

- Anytime the player is reduced to 0 hit points or below, the rebec grants the effects of a *false life* spell on the player as an immediate action giving her 1d10+10 temporary hit points. Unlike the spell, these temporary hit points remain for as long as the fiddler plays. There is no limit to the number of times it can cast *false life*, and it can do so multiple times per round.

- The rebec grants *lesser restoration* upon the fiddler once per day to mitigate any effects of fatigue or exhaustion in order to allow her to keep playing.

- The player remains under the constant effects of a *freedom of movement* spell.

The primary purpose of the rebec is to animate the dead to wretched unlife. Each round that the rebec is played, any corpses within the range of its hearing (including those buried in this range) are subject to reanimation. Even corpses that have rotted away can return as incorporeal undead. For each round of playing in an area where dead bodies are available, roll d6 to determine what type of undead creature that is created. These creatures do not attack the fiddler but are not otherwise under the player's command; they remain true to form, attacking living creatures as opportunity presents. They remain animated until destroyed or the rebec is destroyed at which point all previously animated undead return to death once again.

d6	Undead Type
1–2	skeleton
3–4	zombie
5	ectoplasmic creature[AP43] (see page 10)
6	creature of GMs choice (lesser shadow and ghoul wolf in this adventure)

The effects and powers of the rebec cannot be dispelled or nullified by *silence* or countersong (though countersong will prevent the animation of undead creatures for its duration). The fiddler need not concentrate for the rebec's powers to activate, though she must use a move action each round that does not provoke attacks of opportunity to play the instrument.

DESTRUCTION

The rebec can only be destroyed by sundering it, though it provides a +4 bonus to the fiddler's CMD to resist sundering. It has hardness 5 and 20 hit points. It does not gain the broken condition but when reduced to 0 hit points it is destroyed.

EPILOGUE

When the *Rebec Malevolenti* is destroyed, all undead created by it are immediately destroyed as well. The other powers it provides likewise end immediately. If still alive, Alhindri stops in her tracks. The expression of jubilation and total abandon vanish from her face instantly and are instead replaced by the ashen pallor that once again leeches the color from her cheeks. She is visibly reduced to a shell of her former self becoming completely unresponsive and listless. She will offer no resistance and can easily be slain or led about. Alhindri has become one of the forlorn once again, The twisted work of the Dark Stranger is over for now. Who he was or what his pur- pose may have been remains a mystery to be solved for another day. The townsfolk recognize Alhindri from tales of the massacre and will wish to lynch her to prevent her from being able to come back and threaten the town again at some time it the future. If the PCs can change their attitude from hostile towards her to indifferent, they will agree let the sheriff lock her up until she can be transported back to the asylum from which she escaped.

If the PCs search for Father Grimble and the missing acolytes, they find that one of the burial vaults at the eastern edge of the cemetery has been blocked shut from broken headstones piled against the door. This can be cleared in a matter of minutes, but clearly visible in the dust before this pile is a pair of cloven hoof prints much too large to be a goat or other natural creature. Father Grimble can only state that as he and his acolytes entered the vault in the predawn darkness to prepare it for the coming funeral, the heavy door slammed shut behind them and became held fast. They then began to hear the eerie fiddling and knew something foul was afoot.

This *Aegis of Empires Adventure Path* is coming from Legendary Games! This massive 6-part adventure saga combines danger, intrigue, horror, and the discovery of ancient mysteries in the magnificent **Lost Lands** campaign setting! This incredible world of adventure, developed over 20 years of adventures and accessories from Necromancer Games and Frog God Games, combines old-school pulp fantasy with evocative stories, vividly detailed cultures and politics, and deadly dungeons. Lead developer Greg Vaughan and his terrifically talented team of authors and artists have created a unique series of loosely coupled adventures to be played in sequence but also woven into the fabric of the campaign world, whether one of your own design or delving into the deep lore of the Lost Lands. Discover the secrets of antiquity or be consumed in their seeking as you brave the dark paths of the *Aegis of Empires*!

This amazing adventure saga is available in PDF and softcover for **5th Edition**, *Pathfinder Second Edition,* and the *Pathfinder Roleplaying Game.* In addition to the is early release of the *Aegis of Empires Player's Guide* and the first volume of the adventure path, *The Book in the Old House,* the entire *Aegis of Empires* saga is coming to **Kickstarter** to fund production of a massive compilation and hardcover version for each system.

Note: Anyone purchasing these early releases and also backing the Kickstarter will receive a special credit for their original purchase price at the Legendary Games webstore!

Made in the USA
Coppell, TX
05 October 2024

Intent on his mission, Henry almost didn't see Gloria waiting on the path. He skidded, landed on his backside, then bounced up and said, "I'm okay!" Gloria looked concerned. Henry joked, "Did you see that lizard reach out his foot and trip me?"

Gloria giggled, then smiled and motioned toward a large, flat rock.
Wild sweet peas outlined the shape of a heart.

Henry gazed at Gloria. Looking down at her feet, then up at
Henry, she asked, "Henry—will you share a snack with me?"
Henry blinked several times, then bobbed his head up and down
like a pigeon.

After sharing the peas, Henry cleared his throat and said, "I wanted to impress you, Gloria, by learning a new dance."
Gloria and Henry looked at each other, and all at once knew they had the same brilliant idea.

Flamenco!

And they knew just who could teach them!

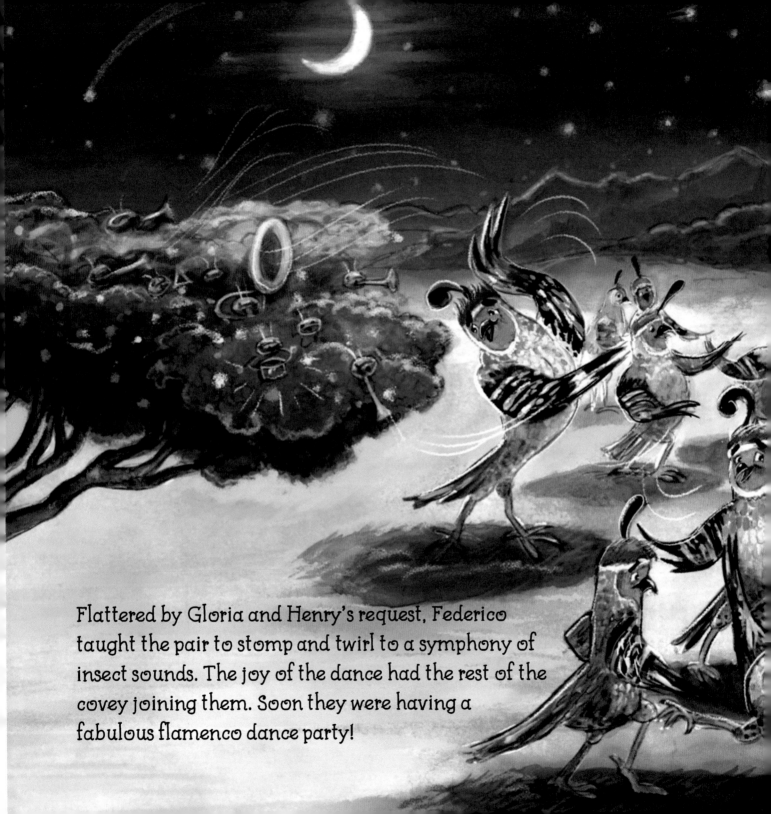

Flattered by Gloria and Henry's request, Federico taught the pair to stomp and twirl to a symphony of insect sounds. The joy of the dance had the rest of the covey joining them. Soon they were having a fabulous flamenco dance party!

Henry's face couldn't stop smiling. Was his heart smiling too? Henry wondered.

Just In Case You Wondered...
*Birds that are not native to the Rio Grande bosque

blue-footed booby* – a brown bird known for its large blue feet and high-stepping dance

bosque (boss-kee) - Spanish word for forest; a small area of trees or brush along the riverbanks in the southwestern part of the United States

cottonwood – large trees found in the bosque along the Rio Grande; their cotton-like seeds float in the breeze

covey – a community of quails

crest – a bunch of feathers on top of a bird's head

flamenco (fluh-men-ko) – a rhythmic Spanish dance

flamingo* – a tall pink bird known for standing on one leg

grey crowned crane* – a bird with a black and white face and a stiff gold crown of feathers on its head

Himalayan monal* – a colorful bird with a ponytail of feathers on its head

hoopoe* – an orange bird with a zebra-striped mohawk on its head

macaroni penguin* – a black and white bird with yellow feathers on its head; a bird that looks as though it is wearing a tuxedo and yellow toupee

quail – a sociable small bird that rarely flies

Rio Grande (ree-oh grahn-day) – Spanish for big river; a river that begins in Colorado and flows through New Mexico to the Gulf of Mexico

roo – a male quail

Just for Fun

Among the exotic birds, can you spot the quail?

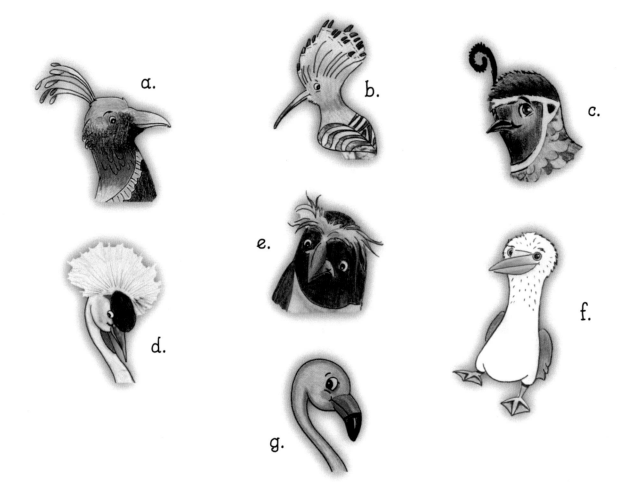

a.

b.

c.

d.

e.

f.

g.

Answer: a. Himalayan monal, b. hoopoe, c. quail, d. grey crowned crane, e. macaroni penguin, f. blue-footed booby, g. flamingo

---

Trivia: What is a group of quails called?

Answer: a covey

About the Editor: Nevin Mays is a children's book addict, dog editor and chocolate cuddler... and sometimes makes embarrassing malapropisms! As a freelancer editor, she helps authors and publishers create and polish picture books, chapter books, and novels for kids and teens. She has experience in many mediums, including audiobooks, interactive ebooks, and novelty books. You can find her at www.nevinmays.com.

About the Illustrator: Kim Sponaugle uses her God-given talent to leave a mark on the heart. Her style can be described as render-based traditional, using vibrant watercolor. Her strength is in creating emotion through action. Her art converges somewhere in the sweet spot of whimsy where realistic and cartoon meet. You can find her at www.picturekitchenstudio.com.

Author's Note: My inspiration for *Henry Wondered* is the desert quail who live in my native Land of Enchantment. I became acquainted with them during my many walks along the arroyos. You may also like to know that when I was a little girl, I confused flamenco with flamingo and wondered why the dancers did not stand on one foot and wear pink.

Thank you for reading *Henry Wondered*. I hope it made you smile and want to share it with your family and friends. Your feedback is important, so I hope you take time to post a review.

Henry and Friends Series

Henry Wondered. A Story About Jealousy, Serendipity and . . . Flamenco!
Book one of the Henry and Friends Series

Federico Exaggerated. A Story About Tall Tales, Honesty, and . . . The Boldest Berry!
Book two of the Henry and Friends Series

Gloria Smiled. A Story About Disappointment, Resilience, and . . . The Sorpresa!
Book three of the Henry and Friends Series

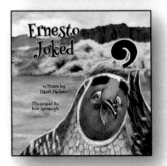

Ernesto Joked. A Story About Humor, Courage, and . . . Señor Coyoté!
Book four of the Henry and Friends Series

Ever wish you could capture
your parent's childhood
memories?

This is a tribute to childhood
back when...

That's How It Was
Operation Finders Keepers

By Hazel Pacheco

Made in the USA
Coppell, TX
05 October 2024